Lennox Berkeley
1903 – 1989

Sonatina

for Treble Recorder and Piano
für Altblockflöte und Klavier

OFB 1040
ISMN 979-0-2201-1703-9

www.schott-music.com

Mainz · London · Berlin · Madrid · New York · Paris · Prague · Tokyo · Toronto
© 1940 SCHOTT MUSIC Ltd, London · Printed in Germany

SONATINA

LENNOX BERKELEY

I.

4

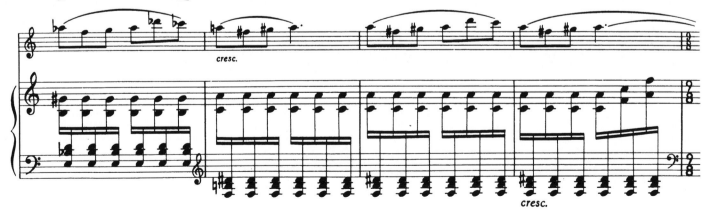

6

SONATINA

TREBLE RECORDER
(or Flute)

I.

LENNOX BERKELEY

TREBLE RECORDER (or Flute)

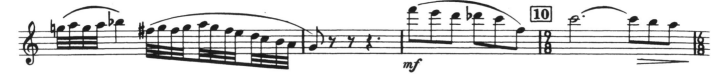

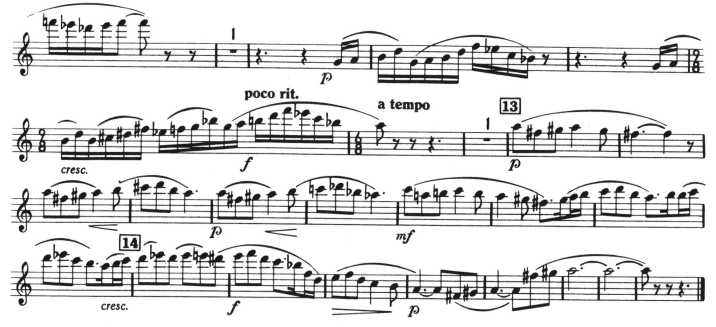

II.

III.

II.

III.

Allegro moderato ($\dotted = $ 112)

poco rit. **21** a tempo

12